Name: John Gilham _____

Address: _____

_____

EDITORIAL Editors: David Leach, Kate Lloyd • **Designer**: Donna Askem • Thanks to Lauren McPhee

TITAN COMICS Senior Comics Editor: Martin Eden • **Production Supervisors** Jackie Flook, Maria Pearson • **Production Assistant** Peter James • **Art Director** Oz Browne
Circulation Manager Steve Tothill • **Direct Sales & Marketing Manager** Ricky Claydon • **Marketing Assistant** Rebecca Lonergan • **Commercial Manager** Michelle Fairlamb
Publishing Manager Darryl Tothill • **Publishing Director** Chris Teather • **Operations Director** Leigh Baulch
• **Executive Director** Vivian Cheung • **Publisher** Nick Landau

ADVENTURE TIME Annual 2017

ISBN: 9781785853241

CONTENTS

Greetings fellow adventurers, see how many times you can find me hiding out in this annual! Turn to page 70 for the answer.

LAUNDROMARCELINE

BY LUCY KNISLEY

Scrub away the monster guts,
The stinky pants
that smell like butts...

...Wash
those blankets,
soap those sheets,
clean those socks
that smell
like feets!

YES!

Laundry time!

Open it,
dude!

Let's smell
that soapy
goodness.

YIPES!

What!?

Everything's RED!

Uh oh!

Huff Huff

PHEW!

At least my sock is okay.

Jake! Your red sock REDDIFIED all this stuff!

And you don't even wear socks!

Rub

Rub

Well, naw, not usually...

But just lookit how great this thing is!

What's up?

Oof

DUMP

There was a red-splosion in my laundry. I was hoping you could help fix it!

WHAT

You want me...

A vampire **queen**...

...to do...

...Your LAUNDRY?

Wait! Wait! Marceline!

I can help you in exchange! Do chores, whatever!

Oh.

Actually there **are** a few things you could do around here...

Oh. My. Glob.

You look ADORABLE.

That is hilarious!

Marceline. C'mon, de-red this stuff like you promised.

SIGH FINE.

SLURP

Thanks, Marceline!

Uh oh...

My sock! Is it okay?

Oh! Yeah, dude, it's fine.

END

11

PUZZLE TIME

MARCELINE'S BLOODCURDLING BRAINTEASERS!

SPOOKY SUDOOOKU

Marceline's a radical dame who likes to play games, but she'll also dingle your bones into tapioca pudding if she feels like it. Complete this puzzle by writing the correct letters in the empty spaces. Every row, column and 4x4 mini grid must have one of each type of monstrous Marcie.

A = ⬤ B = ⬤ C = ⬤ D = ⬤

PRINCESS IN PERIL!

Oh. My. Glob. Dramabomb! LSP has gotten herself trapped in a dungeon Ooo-zing with monsters. Can you help Her Royal Lumpiness find her way out of this far-too-dangerous, incredible place?

EXIT!

BRAIN STRAIN!

Wowcowchow, dudes, the Brain Beast has totes got itself into a terrible tangle. Can you piece back together this unspeakably evil creature so that Finn and Jake can kill it dead dead? We've done the first one for you: 1 = F.

Turn to page 70 for the rest of the answers

1
2
3
4
5
6
7
8

A
B
C
D
E
F
G
H

So instead, I just crammed more eggs in there!

Of course! What else can you do?

Right! But when I ran out of eggs I had to squirt in some mayonnaise and that only made it wo--

Knock knock! Hey guys, sorry I'm late--I had some stuff to take care of first.

KNOCK KNOCK

Oh, hey you!

Glad you could make it!

Ha! You look awesome. So are you ready? Because it's **ADVENTURE SEASON**, and I'm looking for a quencher for my thirst for adventure!!

I'm ready. I put on the adventure suit you made me, didn't I?

Let's do this!! **WHAT TIME IS IT??**

Hold up brotimes, I've got a better question! **WHAT PHRASE RESULTS FROM SAYING "ADVENTURE" AND THEN THE OBJECT FORM OF THE FIRST-PERSON SINGULAR NOMINATIVE CASE PERSONAL PRONOUN??**

Um. Adventure... me?

ADVENTURE TIME

In **OUR** experience, sometimes adventure comes to you, but other times you have to go looking for it!

Like trouble?

Exactly!

Sometimes they're actually kinda hard to tell apart.

Dude, trouble's just an adventure you haven't finished yet!

But I--um, I don't see any adventure here. You see anything, Jake? Pretty sure adventure was supposed to be here, like, five minutes ago.

I mean, that aquatic bird kinda looks like he means business.

Aquatic bird, huh? Hey, since you're the special guest, why don't you take a peek?

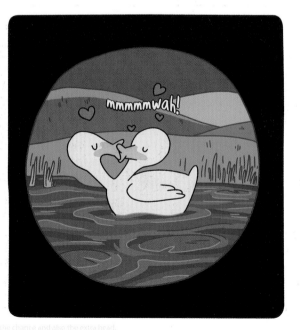

mmmmmwah!

Guys, all I saw was a duck making out with itself.

I WANNA SEE!!

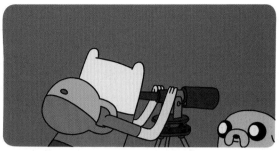

I'm not sure what I was expecting.

Okay, **OBVIOUSLY** there's no adventure nearby right now. That's fine! We'll just go downstairs and find out why adventure's late as buns!

Hey, did you like your adventuring boots?

Yeah! The other one says "ADVENTURES".

CHECK OUT THESE SWEET BOOTS! I GOT THEM FROM MY FRIENDS FOR WHEN I GO ON

Heh. Yeah, Finn did those. Sometimes I write things on my legs, like "WHAT'S UP LADIES?" or "HEY, MY FACE IS UP THERE!" or "IF YOU KEEP GOING DOWN YOU'RE JUST GONNA FIND STINKY OL' FEET, DUMMY."

I've also used "WHAT A PIECE OF WORK ARE MY LEGS! HOW NOBLE IN GAMS, HOW INFINITE IN QUADS!", which, and I honestly say this humbly, is totally fair. One time I even--hey!

Are you yawning?!

You are yawning!! You insult not only Jake but, ME, the guy who wrote this comic! I can't believe this. I swear, the next four issues are gonna be called "FINN AND JAKE LEARN TO BE POLITE." YOU, AS THE READER, SHOULD PROBABLY BE TAKING NOTES."

Dude, **OBVIOUSLY** it's hard to go to bed at a reasonable hour--**BELIEVE ME, I KNOW**--but it's still rude to yawn when I'm talking up quads! I--

SMACK!

FINN!!

Hey, don't try to distract me. I'm here to talk down to you about bedtimes, **NOT** to be distracted when you shout my friend's name! Although, getting distracted right now **IS** a tantalizing possibility... huh! I wonder what Finn's up to?

Why, I suppose I could spare a **PARTIAL** turn-around to see what's going on with my ol' buddy Finn. But that's it! After I've completed this partial turn, I've still got **LOTS** of opinions about bedtimes to share.

Gah!!

SMACK

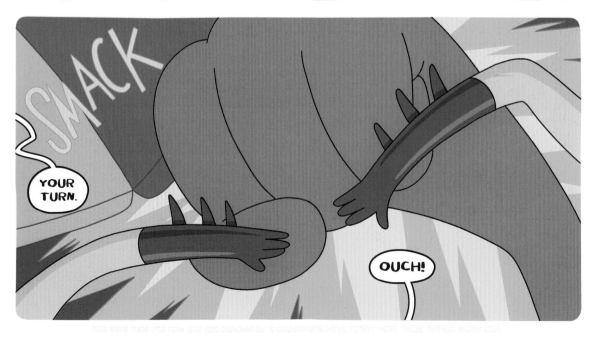

SMACK

YOUR TURN.

OUCH!

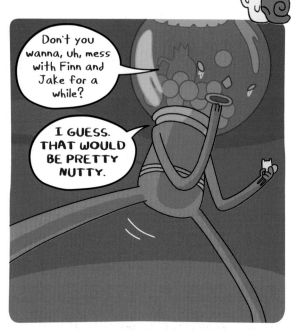

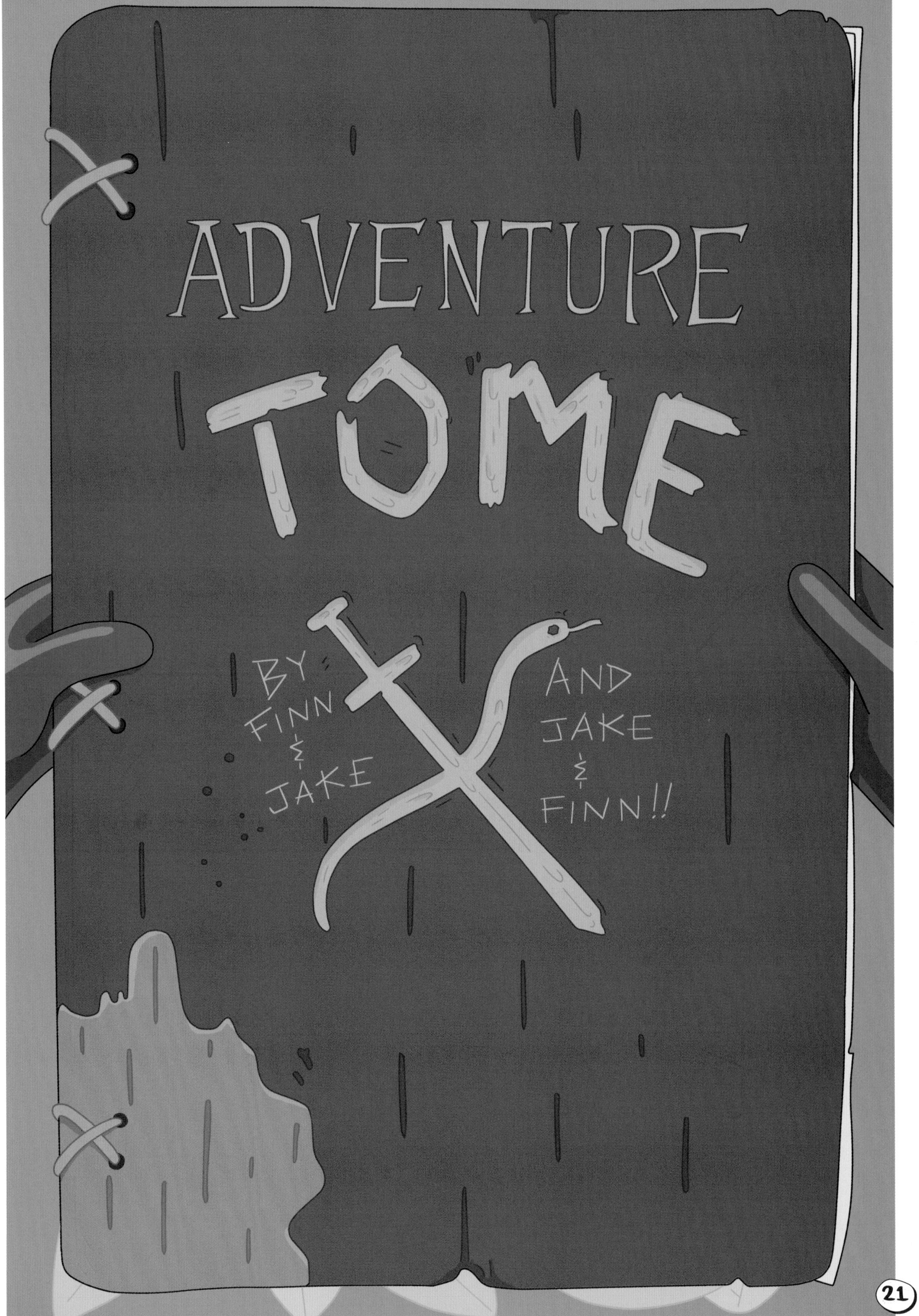
ADVENTURE
TOME
BY FINN & JAKE
AND JAKE & FINN!!

GOOD PLACES
for Adventures

UP on the ROOF
- only sometimes adventures are had here.
— not so good during knife storms

CaNDY KINGDOM
AKA "Shenanigan Central"
x We've got an "IN" with the Head of State

THE WOODLANDS clear and COOL
* Cool place to learn nature stuff
MANY gross bugs can be found under Rocks.

SAW A COOL DEER HERE ONCE 2 (had shades + backwards cap)

FIRE KINGDOM
BE SURE TO BRING MAGIC OR BE DOWN WITH GETTING HECKA BURNED

CITY of THIEVES
IF you go here everything you own will get stolen!!! INCLUDING YOUR HEART!
- Actually that's not true, it's not that great.

BREAKFAST KINGDOM
- DO NOT GO WHEN HUNGRY!
- DO NOT GO IN THE LATE AFTERNOON EITHER, IT'S FULL OF BREAKFASTS THAT HAVE BEEN LEFT OUT ALL DAY

GLOB Land
← SOUNDS NEAT!
* Probably rad parties there ?? Worth investigating eventually.

Whirlpool OF SHARKS
FUN for at least a little while...

Whirlpool OF WHALES
- WHALE OF A GOOD TIME -
- by that I mean they hug you and feed you shrimp.
+ It's pretty rad, gotta say

CLOUD LAND
hard to get to
- everyone there made out of clouds
- Sucks to breathe in a pal by mistake
- although honestly, it's kinda fun to breathe in a pal by mistake

BLOOD LAND
x Not what it sounds like, actually more of a plasma grotto

ICE KINGDOM
Good Place to go if you think "Adventure" means "hanging out with adult senior"

ISLE OF STEAM
↳ Nice place to relax

LUMPY SPACE
ONLY accessible through portal, the password is "Whatevers" and then the TOTAL NUMBER of cans of beans you've eaten so far this year

LUMPY SPACE residents will call you "Smoothies" — which is fine because Smoothies are a delicious treat any time of day

MOUNT CRAGDOR
A mountain full of challenges for ADVENTURERS! BEST PLACE EVER

We should go back sometime, Yo!

ENEMIES AND FRENEMIES

Who sometimes get all up in our fries.

LICH

- TOTALLY DEAD FOR 100% REAL +HIS TIME.
- Hard to beat (Final boss level abilities?? IT'S NUTS!)

ICE KING

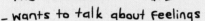

- weird old man, smells like cold socks
- wants to talk about feelings
- easily defeated, just dodge his ice and punch him.

#1 BABE???

8-HEAD TED → only one of his heads is evil; the other 7 are pretty chill, actually.

SIR SLICER

SENTIENT HOUSE THAT DOES NOT RESPOND TO STIMULI

- hard to tell if actually sentient but I'm PRETTY sure it is.

EARL of LEMONGRAB

- This guy, oh my glob, this guy
- defeated by earplugs so you can ignore him
- if he offers to let you look inside his mouth SAY NO.

MAN, FORGET THIS GUY!

↑ defeated by heavy armor AND/OR hubris

RICARDIO

- one of the several alive Ice king body parts we've had to defeat already
- GROSS
- Why is this so gross.

MISS ADVENTURE

Sounds like she'd be rad, but instead she keeps getting us into mis-adventures where things KEEP GOING WRONG.

→ ospect is not h a rprise.

Princess Bubblegum

- Not an enemy! She is really smart and nice
- She is a real special lady and I'm glad we're friends ♡

HUNSON ABADEER

- Marceline's dad: It's weird around your friend's parents sometimes
* -ALSO he's evil.

ASH
- what a tool, nobody likes him
- I owe him like, 30 punches.

GUNTER

DO NOT ENGAGE!

* MAGIC MAN

- WHAT A JERK! HE IS THE ONE WHO SHOULD EAT IT, NOT ME
- used to be real cool? I don't buy it
- defeat him by never talking to him in the first place. HE'S A JERK!

Lady Stabsworth Z. Backwash III

- It's really unlikely that someone born with such a name would live up to it perfectly but here we are.

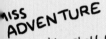

SUPER SPECIAL FIGHT MOVES
(TOP SECRET)

BELLY OF THE BRO

Jake shrinks down and hides inside Finn's belly.

"PLANET JAKE"

Jake stretches out to cover the entire planet in a thin film of JAKE, then when the bad guy least suspects it, he POPS up a hand to punch 'em.

CROUCHING TIGER

We hide behind a Tiger, bad guy will probably be too scared to investigate.

SNOWSUIT JAKE

useful on ice missions when legs get cold.

JAKE HANDS

Jake turns into a giant fist that goes over Finn's fist so he can punch with JAKE.

Better than it sounds! and it already sounds AMAZING

JAKE HOLE

Finn hides in a hole, enemy says "Hey are you in that hole?" Jake punches them down the hole and when they land Finn punches them again just to be safe

BOOMERFINN

Finn is thrown like a Boomerang, punches the bad guy in mid air and then returns to Jake.

UNATTEMPTED but what could possibly go wrong??

SPACE ELEVATOR JAKE

Jake turns into an elevator to SPACE (useful on space missions if they ever happen again.)

THE SUBMICRON DISS

Jake rearranges the atoms of someone's face so at a microscopic level they spell out "IM A DUMMY" and the bad guy doesn't know until Finn says "HAHA you sure are!!" then they realize the truth.

JAKE SUIT

Honestly why we don't do this 24/7 is my question.

FINN SUIT

This really hurt the last time we tried it.
—Finn

SAWBLADE EYES JAKE

Remember not to rub your eyes.

FRACTAL GLOB JAKE

SAW THIS IN THE FUTURE, TOTALLY AWESOME.

BELLYTIME FINN

Finn eats a lot and then enemies get distracted by his SpecTACULAR belly (good "always on" fight move.)

MECHAJAKE WITH ADVENTURE-READY FINN
featuring karate-chop action

Nothing bad could possibly happen in this form.

?

WOW THERE'S PROBABLY OTHER BATTLE TECHNIQUES BUT I CAN'T THINK OF ANY RIGHT NOW.

Sometimes a brother just has to IMPROVISE, yo.

Dudes, yo, that book was pretty useless! But I'm gonna **IMPROVISE**.

SUPER SPECIAL FIGHT MOVES

TOP 10 CANDY KINGDOM ADVENTURES

Finn, ask for a gumball and don't forget to be polite! Ice King, be the gumball--then you'll be able to reset him from the inside during the gumball purchase process!

What? No! I'm not going in there! I don't know where those gumballs come out!!

Come on, it's not hard! Here. **I'LL DO IT.**

I'm still a valued member of the team! I just don't wanna get swallowed--that doesn't make me a bad Ice King! That doesn't make me weird!

Ready, Finn?

Ready when you are!!

Three...

Two...

One...

NOW, Finn!!

Excuse me, Gumball Guardian! **I'D LIKE TO HAVE A GUMBALL, PLEASE!!**

GUMBALL GUARDIANS REWARD POLITENESS. ENJOY YOUR REWARD. IT IS A GIANT GUMBALL AND IT IS COMING OUT OF ME NOW.

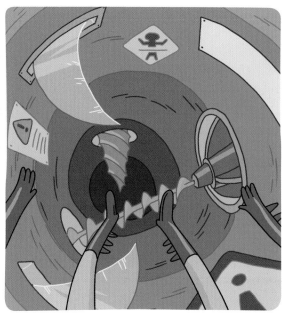

GUARDIAN COLD RESET MANUAL TOGGLE

KA-CHOOM

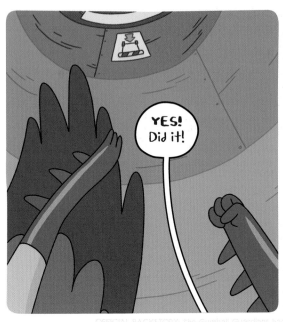

YES! Did it!

CLANGGG

RESET COMPLETE. HELLO. I AM AT... FINN AND JAKE'S HOUSE? I AM APPARENTLY NEGLIGENT IN MY DUTIES AND HAVE SUFFERED COSMETIC DAMAGE TO MY SWEET HEAD. I MUST RETURN TO THE CANDY KINGDOM. GOODBYE.

PTOIE

What the butt, dude? Why'd you make him crazy in the first place??

S'yeah! What all the butts!

Help me up and I'll explain everything!

Thanks. Hey now, how'd you get your gauntlets so... so touchably soft?

Ice King!!

Look, it's a long story. You guys wanna hear about it with visual aids? I can make ice sculptures showing what happened!

YES.

BUT ONLY BECAUSE I REALLY LOVE VISUAL AIDS.

Well, it's a pretty classic story. I found two crystals or whatever and stuck 'em inside the Gumball Guardian's head, **AS ONE DOES**. Only it turns out that they put him under my control and made him obey my next two commands! First I asked him what it's like to be so tall.

And he was all **"BEING TALL'S OKAY. I DON'T REALLY KNOW WHAT IT'S LIKE TO BE ANYTHING ELSE?"**

Pretty sweet, I know! Then he said **"WHAT SHOULD I DO NOW, MASTER?"** and I said "What am I, your mom? Who cares? Go do whatever! Go nuts!"

And uh, you guys know the rest. He came here and punched up the place.

MIND-CONTROL CRYSTALS?! We never talked about that! This was supposed to be a fun afternoon, not a fun afternoon **THAT PUTS US ALL IN DANGER!**

Huh?

I mean, um, ha ha, we sure **DIDN'T** know that an adventure was going to happen today!

Yes. To clarify my friend's response, uh, we definitely did **NOT** team up to give you what was supposed to be a fun surprise that went **CRAZY WRONG** because of Ice King.

Yes. This was definitely not part of a plan that I messed up and made **TOO REAL** but only because I **CARE SO MUCH.**

It's cool, guys. I had a great time. Thank you.

Hey, I should be going though. You want your book back?

No no, keep it!

It's a gift: a souvenir from today!

Okay, well--see you later!

Thanks for hanging out today!

Later, skater!

Call me!!

In retrospect these visual aids were actually a lot more work than just telling us what happened, but OH WELL.

PUZZLE TIME

SPOT THE DIFFS!

Looks like Ice King is up to his old tricks again. What a patoot! Can you spot six diffs on picture B!

A

B

PICK OUT THE PENGUINS

Only two of these semi-loyal pets are identical. Can you spot which?

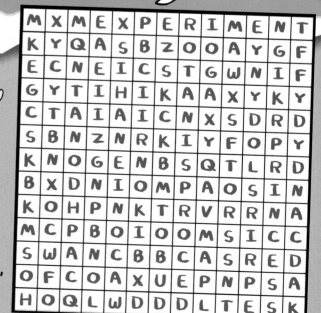

1 2 3 4 5 6 7 8

Turn to page 70 for the answers

PB'S 'WORDY' WORDSEARCH

WHAT THE GLOB! Why am I even on this page?

Brainboxes at the ready! Can you find these words relating to Princess Bubblegum in the grid opposite? Answers can run forwards, backwards, up, down and diagonally.

M	X	M	E	X	P	E	R	I	M	E	N	T
K	Y	Q	A	S	B	Z	O	O	A	Y	G	F
E	C	N	E	I	C	S	T	G	W	N	I	F
G	Y	T	I	H	I	K	A	A	X	Y	K	Y
C	T	A	I	A	I	C	N	X	S	D	R	D
S	B	N	Z	N	R	K	I	Y	F	O	P	Y
K	N	O	G	E	N	B	S	Q	T	L	R	D
B	X	D	N	I	O	M	P	A	O	S	I	N
K	O	H	P	N	K	T	R	V	R	R	N	A
M	C	P	B	O	I	O	O	M	S	I	C	C
S	W	A	N	C	B	B	C	A	S	R	E	D
O	F	C	O	A	X	U	E	P	N	P	S	A
H	O	Q	L	W	D	D	D	L	T	E	S	K

BONNIBEL   PRINCESS
CANDY   PINK
KINGDOM   SCIENCE
DECORPSINATOR   EXPERIMENT
LABORATORY   BRAINY   SWAN

31

My story starts here: Ooo.

65 million years ago. Give or take.

DINOSAUR TIMES.

Only the problem is, dinosaurs couldn't talk, so my story is going to be **PRETTY BORING** unless I start putting words in their mouths.

So check it out, baby!

That the best you got, T-Rex?

I got more! I can bring more!

I didn't know if we were fighting for real or not?

Yeah man, me and my pals are trying to eat you. We're carnivores so wherever we see some meat we want, we just straight-up eat it!

We don't even care if it's bad for us or if our moms say we've had enough meat for one day!

Aw man that sounds awesome!! That just sounds like a really satisfying way to live your life.

Moms: what do they know? A lot? Oh, okay, nevermind then I guess

Dudes, I think I found the gem I was looking for too!

...Dudes?

Aw dudes, y'all fainted from exhaustion! Weaaaaak!! None of you guys said you were a bunch of big ol' babies!

Anyway whatever we got our prizes, so let's outie! You guys coming?

...No?

You're just gonna chill out here forever then, okay?

You stay there, gem! I got plans for you.

This is Chewie calling Hemogobbler! Come in Hemogobbler!

That's not my nickname!

Negatory, Hemogobbler, that's totally your new nickname! Over!

Dude, you don't have to say "over" after each message.

I totally do! Over!

That's what makes walkum talkums awesome! Over!!

Hey Bonnibel, Whatcha playing?

10:00

AHHH!

NOTHING! NOTHING!

Because it kinda looked like you were playing **Buns Punch 2**.

I WAS JUST CURIOUS!

AHHH

LET'S NEVER TALK ABOUT THIS AGAIN, I'D LIKE TO GO HOME NOW PLEASE.

Hey man, it's not like those buns are gonna punch themselves, right?

Here. Take my hand.

Thanks Marceline.

Don't mention it.

Now hold on tight.

So, you saw that, right? Me and Gemma were reunited! It was only briefly, but still! At least now I knew she was okay, and she knew I was too. That was awesome!

My new owner, Marceline — we didn't really hang out much. I spent a lot of time in that chest. It's hard to tell how long.

I guess mainly because there weren't any clocks in there.

It felt like maybe a couple hundred years? I guess?

But eventually, she came for me again...

SMASH!
SMACK!

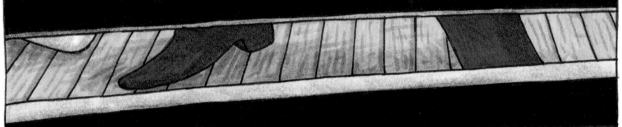

ARGH!

I hate her I hate her seriously I hate her!

"Ooooh, I made my own kingdom, so I'm gonna call myself princess now that I'm way too busy to show up to YOUR things, Marceline!"

Gah!

Who does she think she is??

"Oh, I'm sorry Marceline, I didn't mean to miss your first big gig, it's just I've made myself a stupid boyfriend I call 'Mr. Cream Puff' because that's a real name adults call each other and now I'm gonna hang out with him 24/7!"

"Oh, and your friendship isn't important to me since I'll just make new friends out of CANDY when I glob things up with everyone! And everyone always forgives me because I'm PRINCESS Bubblegum now!"

...dang it.

Wow. I forgot that was still here.

Marceline to Bubblegum. Come in Bubblegum. You there?

...No?

Well, good. Cause I got some things to say to you and I don't want you to hear them.

I'm complicated, alright?

You should know that by now.

Okay, so I'm not stupid. I know our lives are moving us in different directions, okay? I get that. I get that nothing lasts forever, believe me.

But that doesn't mean I have to like it.

It's just— the way you act like nothing's wrong, it makes me SO mad. You know that, right? It makes me feel like I'm the only one who remembers how our friendship USED to be, who sees how it's changing. It feels like a betrayal. It feels lousy, Bonnie. And familiar.

This isn't my first rodeo.

And I know that you've got your hands full with your new kingdom, okay? I get that you're busy, and I want you to be busy. You're doing something so ambitious, so crazy...

I know you can do it. You're gonna be the one who changes the world, Bonnie. I've seen it in you.

But there's gotta be a balance there, you know? A way where we can stay friends, a way where I don't feel so hurt all the time. And it's not all you— I know I've been major cheesed because of this and that's not fun for anyone.

...I'll be a better friend, too.

Listen, I'm gonna come by tomorrow, help you build these Candy Kingdom retaining walls. Maybe we can punch some ooze monsters while we're at it, right? I'd like that. Right in the buns, yo.

You've been my best friend for so long, and we're not gonna lose that. We'll figure this out, Bubblegum.

Huh. "Princess Bubblegum." You know, it actually DOES sound kinda cool.

My friend, the princess.

I think I could get used to that.

Over and out.

Okay I wasn't actually around Bubblegum to make sure she heard that last part but Gemma told me it later so you can trust us on that. It was nice. Sweet, you know?

Anyway, I spent another super long time in that box. I was moved a few times, and eventually lost and forgotten. Another few hundred years, maybe? But I was left alone, until one day I met my new owners. Two of them this time! One was like, a dog?

TAP TAP TAP

Dude, come quick! I found a treasure box in the attic!

I wanna see!!

COOOOOOOL!

Jake, I think this is Marceline's! Like, from when she lived here in history times?

Whoa, no way!! PAL TREASURE!!

I'll be taking THAT!

oof!

Hey!!

What the math, dude?

Man why you gotta steal this thing? We got like, tons of free treasure downstairs!

WE LITERALLY WOULDN'T NOTICE ANY OF THAT MISSING.

THAT treasure is just stuff. But THIS treasure...THIS treasure is suffused with the POWER OF PALTIMES. Once I crack them open and extract their PAL ESSENCE, Princess Bubblegum will want to hang out with ME instead!

Ricardio, your plan is dumb and made of problems!

Hey, that doesn't belong to you! It doesn't even belong to us really!

Hey, what's the deal? I thought Princess Bubblegum totally broke you the last time you got all up in our pineapples!

One thing you should know about broken hearts, Jake...

...give them a little time, and they always get better.

I'm pretty sure that's a metaphor for feelings, not actual dude's hearts that come alive.

Yeah seriously!

Nobody asked you!

Finn, how come bad guys never hug us instead of punching us or lazering us or whatever??

I KNOW RIGHT??

Marceline's amulet fires a lazer. You wanna see what PB's does?

Wait. Is that the one that Shok--

UM OBVIOUSLY I DON'T CARE IF YOU RECOGNIZE IT OR NOT, I JUST WANT YOU TO KNOW THAT IT BRINGS ROBOTS TO LIFE.

OTHERWISE YOU MIGHT NOT'VE UNDERSTOOD HOW AWESOME WHAT I'M ABOUT TO DO IS.

Zappa zup!

Okay Ricardio, I don't know what you think a robot is, but this is a house, so--

--hmm. How do I say this with politeness?

...Maybe you wanna look up "robot" in a dictionary and start from there?

Uh oh.

Aw glob this is either gonna be extremely bad or extremely awesome!

RRRUMMMBLE

Come ooooooon, extremely awesome!!

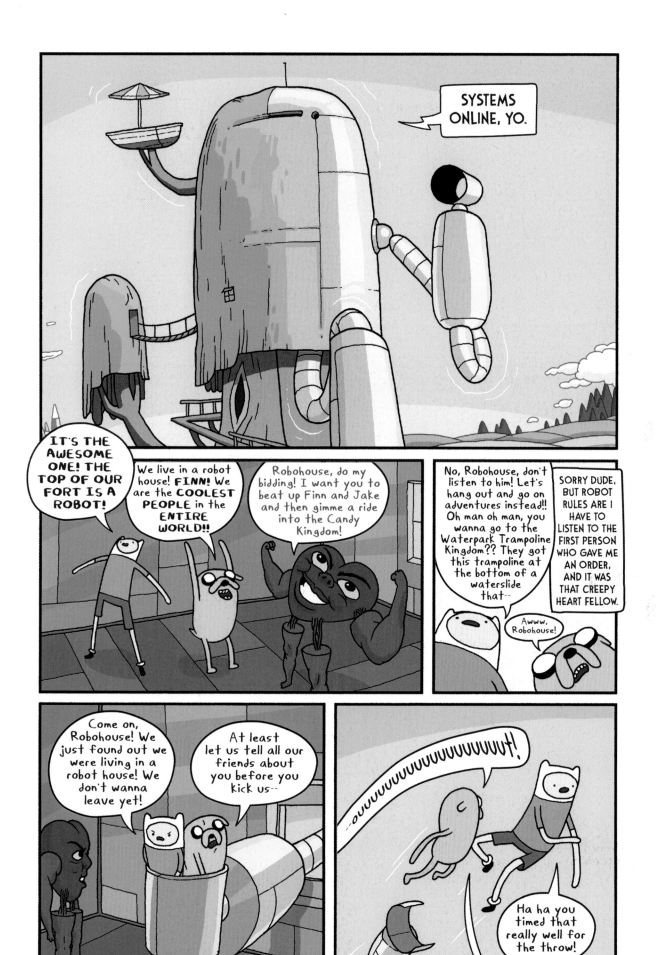

Oh, hey you guys! Did you know we lived in a robot house? Yeah, we're pretty cool. It's no big deal.

Guys, Ricardio just stole my amulet! We tracked him here.

Oh he stole yours too, Marceline! Also, um, we found your stuff and went through it a li'l?

ZOOP!

Wait, he's got YOUR amulet too? You left it there when you moved?

Excuse me, you built a ROBOT into my ROOF?

It was for your own protection, Marceline, and I was only gonna activate it in an emergency! I can't believe YOU left that amulet behind. It was SPECIAL.

I forgot it, okay? I moved out and I forgot it, THE END.

Oh, that makes me feel A LOT better!

Hey guys? Ricardio said that with both amulets he could extract paltime juice from it and make you wanna hang out with him all the time, Peebubs.

Well that's clearly bonkers.

Anyway, what are we waiting for? Ricardio's a jerk and he's messing with our stuff.

Come on, guys...

Let's go break some hearts.

Whoa!

Whoa!!

Gah!

Oh shoot, I guess I should've stopped **YOU** from hitting the ground instead, huh?

It's fine, Jake! I got padding there anyway!

He...he didn't hit me, dude!

Robohouse, it's because--it's because you want us to be pals too, right?? And then we'll live inside of you and whenever anyone thinks of us they'll whisper "so rad" involuntarily?

FAILSAFE. ROBOT CAN'T HARM YOU, MARCELINE! PROGRAMMED THAT WAY!

Aw, Bonnibel.

You always know just what I wanna hear.

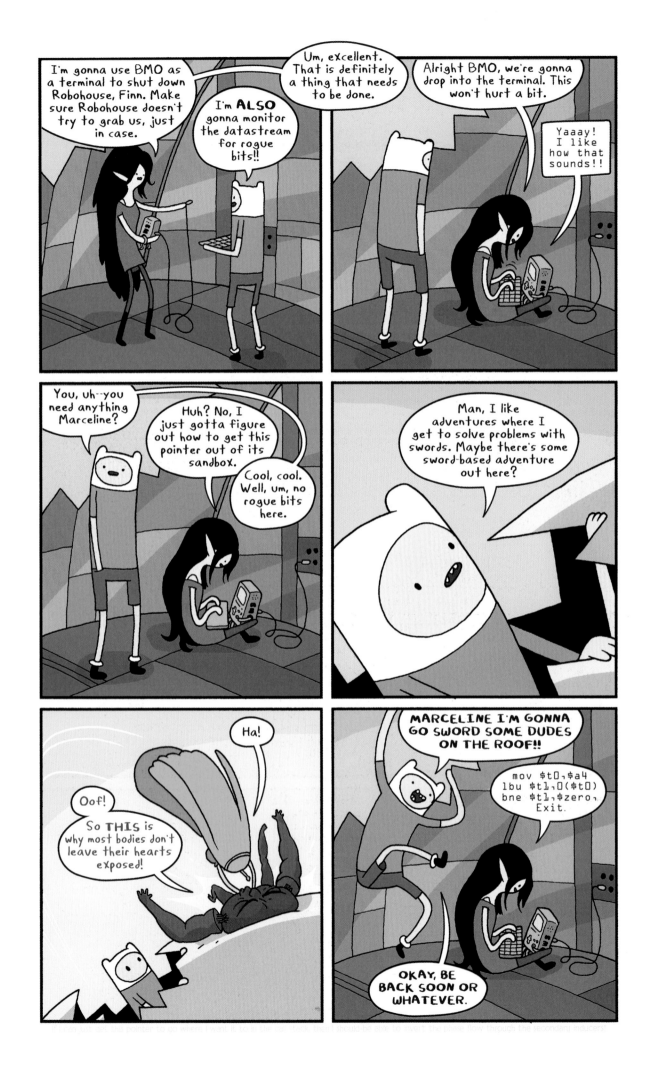

SOON: With Ricardio getting knocked **DIRECTLY** back into Ice King's chest, it seems order has once again been restored to the Candy Kingdom!

This was fun. This was like old times.

Listen, Marceline...do you want your amulet back? Because if you don't it's no big deal, I just--

Bonny. Of course I want it back. And I'm sorry I left it behind.

But you know what? It wasn't just you and me who did this. It was all four of us. **OUR** friendship.

I like that. We could all **SHARE** ownership of the amulets! Like, **PALTIME ARTIFACTS.**

Why don't you hold onto these for now, guys? They'll be a symbol of our awesome friendship. Something to remind us of, you know, ourselves!

Can we keep the chest it came in too?

Yeah dudes.

AHHH IT'LL BE A TREASURE CHEST!

Dude we need to make our own **AMAZING DUNGEON** to put this in!

HEROES ONLY! YES!!

I'd be down helping to build that.

Yeah man.

And now if we're attacked we can go in our own dungeon to bring the house to life again!

And we can shoot our enemies with lazers!! Man!

It's probably **WAY** more fun to be on the other side of the lazer amulet!!

And that's what they did.

Dude, after this you wanna put up 'help wanted' signs for dungeon skeleton warriors?

Um, OBVIOUSLY YES.

A few weeks later, I felt myself being moved, and then...

Again, time passed, and I couldn't tell how long. Years. Decades.

They opened me from time to time, adding new treasure, taking some out, but always Gemma and I remained. Together.

It was so rad. We could finally chill as much as we wanted.

It seemed like the time between their visits was getting longer, but it was okay.

We had each other to keep ourselves company.

I guess it did get a little boring, to be honest. I missed adventure!

Fights! Exploration! Explosions! Making lazers come out of my body!

Anyway!
That totally brings us up to the present. You were the first person worthy enough to get through Finn and Jake's Dungeon of Awesome Surprises and Cool Things Too. It's nice to meet you. I'm Carl.

I'm Gemma.

And now you know my life story.

Our life stories.

There was one thing Princess Bubblegum did have wrong: we were actually magic, and it was the friendship of those four that made us that way.

We're awesome now.

You'll be the first to wear us both together. The first to wield our powers.

Princess Bubblegum. Finn. Marceline. Jake. It's been a long time. I wonder what they're up to now. What distant lands they're in.

I'll miss them, but I can already tell I like you. A lot.

Yeah.
We're gonna get along just great.

Come on.
Grab your friend.

PUZZLE TIME

FINN AND JAKE'S RAD QUEST THINGAMAJIG!

SUMMIT SPECIAL

Oh zang! Mountain Man is having the Lemongrab of all meltdowns. Help Finn and Jake make it to the top before he completely loses it. Which path should the brogends choose?

TOP!

① ② ③

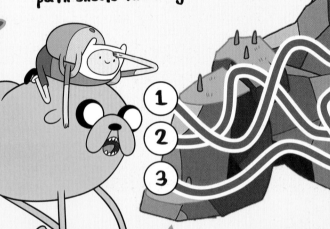

RHOMBUS MYSTERY MEMO

Finn and Jake have been sent a mysterious message. But who the Glob from? And what the stuff does it say? Use the key below to find out!

SYB TFBH, XZM R XLNY LEVI?

R'N IYZOOB YLIVW ZMW TFMGVI PVVKH YOLDRMT RG FK RM SVIV.

RXV PRMT

KEY

A	B	C	D	E	F	G	H	I	J	K	L	M	N	O	P	Q	R	S	T	U	V	W	X	Y	Z
Z	Y	X	W	V	U	T	S	R	Q	P	O	N	M	L	K	J	I	H	G	F	E	D	C	B	A

ODD ANCIENT PSYCHIC TANDEM WAR ELEPHANT OUT!

Which of these Ancient Psychic Tandem War Elephants is diffs from the rest? Finn and Jake totes need his help - so work it out QUICK!

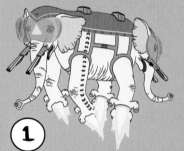
①

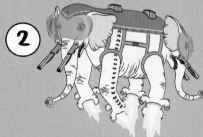
②

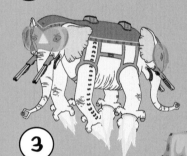
③

④

SAMMICH SEARCH

Jake's hungering for some delish sammiches, but he's dropped his groceries EVERYWHERE. Can you sniff out all 10 items before he goes mega banunununus?

F&J'S WORDS THAT MAKE YOU GO OOO!

Take a gander at these awesome words. Can you spot what they all have in common?

COCOON   MONGOOSE
BOOKWORM   LOOPHOLE
FOOTNOTE   DOORKNOB

IN LIKE FINN

Using the grid below as a guide, copy this totes rhombus pic of Finn into the empty boxes opposite. Then colour Ooo's greatest hero in!

Hey, whaddya mean greatest?

Turn to page 70 for the answers

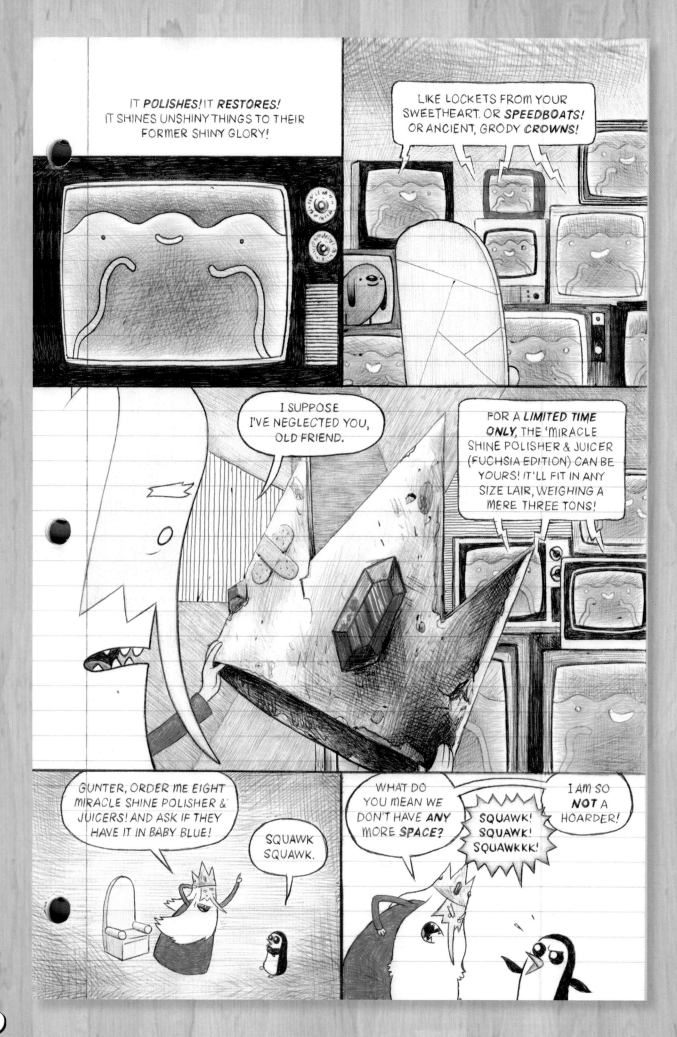

PUZZLE ANSWERS

PAGE 12. MARCELINE'S BLOODCURDLING BRAINTEASERS

SPOOKY SOOODUKU:

PRINCESS IN PERIL:

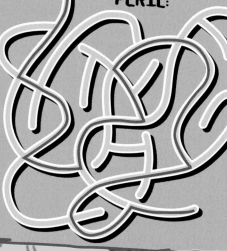

BRAIN STRAIN:
1 = F
2 = C
3 = H
4 = A
5 = G
6 = E
7 = B
8 = D

PAGE 31. ICE KING'S ICY-COOL CONUNDRUMS

SPOT THE DIFFS:

PICK OUT THE PENGUINS:
1 and 8 are identical

PB'S 'WORDY' WORDSEARCH:

PAGES 60&61. FINN AND JAKE'S RAD QUEST THINGAMAJIG!

SUMMIT SPECIAL:
The right path is 2

RHOMBUS MYSTERY MEMO:
HEY GUYS, CAN I COME OVER? I'M REALLY BORED AND GUNTER KEEPS BLOWING IT UP IN HERE. ICE KING

ODD ANCIENT PSYCHIC TANDEM WAR ELEPHANT OUT:
2

F&J'S WORDS THAT MAKE YOU GO OOO:
They all have three Os.

Did you find me? I was on pages 12, 20, 23, 31, 44, 53 and 60.